The Testament of Daedalus

Our sculptors say that if Daedalus were born today and created such works as those that made him famous, he would be laughed at.

PLATO: *The Greater Hippias*

This is the way Daedalus rose
This is the way the sun rejects the shadow.

MICHELANGELO: fragment

Why what a peevish fool was that of Crete
That taught his son the office of a fowl.

SHAKESPEARE:
Henry VI, Part III, Act V, Sc. VI

MICHAEL AYRTON

The Testament of Daedalus

WITH A FOREWORD BY REX WARNER

ROBIN CLARK
London

First published 1962
© Michael Ayrton 1962

First published by Robin Clark Paperback 1991
A member of the Namara Group
27/29 Goodge Street
London W1P 1FD

British Library Cataloguing in Publication Data
Ayrton, Michael, 1921–1975
The testament of Daedalus
I. Title
823.914 [F]
ISBN 0 86072 140X

Printed and bound in Great Britain by
Cox & Wyman Ltd. Reading, Berks.

Contents

Line illustrations
in text

Foreword

Michael Ayrton displays a versatility which, though common enough in the past, is now, unfortunately, a rare thing. I have even heard him criticized just for this particular merit as though there were something reprehensible in being able to do, not one, but many things well. It is hard to fathom the minds of such critics. Presumably the contention is that no one can excel in more than one art. This dogma is contradicted by experience. One has only to think of the fifteenth century Italians and indeed many others. Even Browning is rather inept on this subject:

> 'Does he paint? he fain would write a poem.
> Does he write? he fain would paint a picture.'

True, he regards this as very moving, but implies that it should only be done

> 'Once and only once and for one only . . .'

and he finds it curiously appropriate that Raphael's sonnets have been lost and that Dante never finished his picture.

To me it seems fortunate and admirable that Michael Ayrton is capable of excellence not only in painting and sculpture, but also in writing, and in this particular case of *The Testament of Daedalus* it seems that he has been peculiarly successful. His exhibition of work on the theme of Icarus was justly admired for itself – it can stand alone – so can this literary work of prose and poetry. But each throws light on the other.

The myth of Daedalus and Icarus has something in common with that other great symbolic myth of Prometheus. To venture innovation is to offend. To raise man up to civilization from the apelike condition to which he was called is to invite the retribution of the conservative and stabilizing powers of heaven. To cross the barrier of earth and spread wings in a different element is to break a natural law and must call for punishment. And yet we know that it is also man's nature and excellence to break the rules. Life is impossible without revolution.

The abiding strength and value of these myths is in the fact that both opposites are true. Change is admirable, but a substratum of permanence is essential. An excess of motion will lead to disintegration; a persistent stability must end in a return from life to the mineral state.

Michael Ayrton, as he tells us in his postscript, has been for years 'obsessed' by the myth of Daedalus and his son. He has found in it general and personal meanings, and it would be impertinent here to attempt to summarize them. They are only to be expressed in art, and in this case the expression is remarkable not only for its beauty, but for its clarity.

For his own particular purpose it may be that the Daedalus story had more to offer even than the story of Prometheus; for, in this imagined character of Daedalus, the master craftsman, inventor and first sculptor, he is able to explore the particular

4

problems of the artist, while Icarus can become, in a sense, more generalized and at the same time more precisely modern.

The complexity with which these two characters have been drawn is a measure of the very deep levels which Ayrton has reached in his 'obsession'. The simplicity of the presentation is an indication of his success. There is nothing diffuse or artificial in the combination of prose and poetry. The lyrics have the beauty of being both surprising and natural.

Readers will find their own meanings; some, no doubt, the same as those deliberately found by the author, some personal to themselves. For this story has the profundity and the coruscation of poetry. The slow work of interpretation has been crowned by revelation. It is a task completed of which Daedalus himself might have been proud.

REX WARNER

The Testament of Daedalus

My name is Daedalus. I am a man and a technician. My name means 'bright' and 'cunningly wrought' and also 'the maker of beautiful things', so that I am credited with a variety of satisfactory and necessary inventions, among them bronze casting, the ball and socket joint, tools with which to carve stone, and other utilitarian things including a type of wing which can carry men into the sky and perhaps beyond. As luck will have it many of the inventions previously attributed to Prometheus are now accredited to me, with no justification beyond the desire of Zeus to belittle Prometheus; but that is part of the passage of time, which can erode justice and distort facts. You who read this testament and have known until now only the bare bones of the story will see how time alters and distorts matters, whilst seeming to make them clear.

I assume you have heard of me. I am a technician but I am also a legend so that I survive suspended in a solution of memory. What I write here will seem to have been written several thousand years ago, yet clearly I am writing it today. In the liquid which contains legend suspended there are no problems of date and none of depth, nor is this fluid bounded measurably. It cannot be plumbed nor can its boundaries be charted. Soundings taken will be illusory. You who hang high in these tidal waters, where there seems to be light, may look up and see shreds of cloud moving on the ceiling of the dark sky or you may look down into the depths and discern, shifting and swaying, the weeds of memory clinging to the rocks of the deep past. Which is which will depend upon you. It will depend on your decision as to which way up you hang, for you also swim suspended in this solution and the tides which drag you about in it are capricious.

If I am to explain myself, as I must from time to time, and to explain the curious behaviour of my son Icarus, it is important that you do not see me as more remarkable than I am, simply because my reputation has long been established. I am not a god and have never been made one, despite the abrasive of time, which sometimes grinds men into divine shapes. I am not exactly an immortal and certainly not an oracle. I am not a poet and I am certainly not a hero. That was my son's role and he played it fully with a proper degree of foolishness mixed with glory. I am, as I have said, a technician and being concerned with techniques I am not deeply concerned with myself. If I were I should not be so laborious in describing myself. I should prefer you to see me as a cloudy and noble figure and that would be my privilege as a myth. However, I am determined to establish a frame of reference rather than perpetuate a dream. It is my son who chose to be an enigma. He preferred the posthumous honours of a hero to any sensible achievement and he pays for them by remaining a celebrated shadow whose one splendid moment is his monument.

I must try to make it clear in what relation I stand to my son and he to me. When you hear him speak it will be in some kind of verse which he thinks proper to a hero. I do not altogether understand what he means because his voice is an echo like the sea heard in a seashell, a sound which is known not to be the sea but a movement of trapped air which rustles like breaking waves. He speaks either in fragments or through me. There are ambiguities contained in his words and the very sound of his voice is not more real than this unreal sea-sound in the shell. Therefore, I am uncertain. I shall report what he said during the two days and nights we spent over the sea flying north and west from Crete, but you must understand that very little of it is addressed to me – perhaps some of his words are levelled against me. All that you will hear from Icarus are shards of songs and you will hear them faintly. There are also problems of time which are difficult to establish in words.

These problems, of course, arise from your supposition that you yourself are at a point in time and that my voice comes whispering to you out of a remote past. Perhaps you will conjure some recollection of Minoan artifacts or think us creatures polished from the honey-coloured stone, the faceless figures of the Cyclades, or hear our words linked like a gold-leaved diadem long lying in a grave. Archaeology doubtless colours the mystery for you but I assure it is neither here nor there to me. Consider how you lie in the sea yourself. Does the sun shine down on you or up?

I know my own repetitions and many of my names which come and go. I am still here. Icarus, my son, bore different names at the time when men first fought each other in the sky. He has been multiplied and died in squadrons. He has been called many names when they seemed relevant to particular situations, but this testament is not history and to treat it as history would only serve to plot time upon a fallacious chart, marking as islands those patches of floating weed which move and change in the current.

If you must see this story in time, look only at the gap which spans the millennia between our days of flight and the moment in which you live, the moment yesterday when Icarus leaped into the sky again and fought two wars, spilling death on whole cities. In this time he returned to Crete and conquered it from the air and this was the first land ever to be so conquered. That is the kind of irony the gods enjoy, since it is stained with blood and may be interpreted as a long-postponed revenge. As you read this testament he leaps further towards his antagonist, beyond the envelope which is your present, which to you is now.

It will be in your mind, like the little wings pinned on the breast, or the crew-cut crew, rubber-faced under the pressure of velocity, in the cramped womb cluttered with dials. Perhaps these are numerous and specific people to you. To me they remain single and specific. They remain Icarus. But for purposes of keeping the story within reasonable bounds I shall tell it in its first version, partly because it is remote from you and you will prefer the facts to be pumiced by the passage of years so that they will look to you as clean as pebbles on the shore. On the other hand, I do not wish you to imagine that I have gone, that a myth is musty or a legend survives only because the deep past is pleasantly mysterious. But of course you know that.

Firstly for myself, my usual name is Daedalus. If it means 'bright' I accept that. If it means 'cunningly wrought' that would be just, but if it means 'maker of beautiful things' I should not have given it to myself since I am impatient of aesthetic pretension. I make things cunningly and with skill and if they are beautiful I am not displeased. What there is in me of *poesis* rests in my finger tips and in my eyes, but because the poem exists in the thing I make, when I make it, and not in me, it comes to me in the act of discovery. I make votives of one sort and another and celebrate possibilities in gold and bronze and other materials. In the making of things and especially in the making of images, lies an act of conquest which is sufficient exercise of power for a proper man. That is my view. I seek order. I seek a measured harmony. I seek balance. I seek to avoid pretension although in this I am not invariably successful. I take pleasure in combat with intractable substances and difficult circumstances and I compel them to quiet between my hands. I am not in any way given to dreaming nor to ambition beyond the high practice of my craft, although I enjoy my fame. Icarus is more famous than I am, although he had no particular skill and could not be described as a maker of anything, except his own death, which he contrived in a vainglorious and very poetic manner. He is, however, more famous than I am and perhaps I resent that.

Icarus was first and last a fool. He did not become a man, although he became an immortal. I do not think he has ever discovered who he is. He had pride, such pride that the god himself could scarcely match it and when Icarus flew at the god to cast him down, which is the climax of his story, the god spurned him as you would expect. This was to be expected, but from the pain of it I do not seem to recover.

So Icarus died and I do not think he conquered death, yet he became immortal and this is the central paradox. It is not one Icarus himself would have understood at the time and I doubt if he ever could. The bones of the legend which grew out of our flight and the death, if death it was, of Icarus are bare bones and bleached. It is common knowledge that I made our wings partly of wax and also of other materials. Wax is a useful substance and I use it for many things, among them the 'lost wax' method of bronze casting, as many sculptors have done since. The common story goes that Icarus flew too near the sun and caused the waxen parts of his wings to melt and thus fell into the sea and was drowned. This kind of partial truth, like wax, is malleable and is the stuff of legend, but in fact, as you will presently read, Icarus would have burned and fallen no matter how I had contrived his wings. Had they been iron they would have melted. If they had been stone they would have cindered in the stare of the god and streamed like lava down the sky.

My own flight inspired no one for many years. It was successful. Technically, the wings were adequate, although the camber was a little shallow and the design of wings has been much improved since then. But this testament primarily concerns my son and it is, in the general domain, so bare and so little understood that I have set myself to tell the whole story of Icarus and of our flight from Minos, King of Crete.

I loved Icarus and I have tried to understand him. I do not deny the splendour of his apparent death. Such foolishness has a glory about it and that glory he left behind him in the wreckage of his wings, and that is all he left. Icarus did not love me, he loved only the god and the god he resented. Resentment made him a hero, for this is how heroes are made and undoubtedly he was a hero of sorts. What else could he be? He was my son and he had no talent.

Icarus had no love for order and was clumsy with his hands. It was essential to him that he should become a hero. That is quite comprehensible. Yet I, who bring order, measuring to make harmony, brought him to his disorder, so that he fell. His flight and his wings were of my making. His flight was mine.

To explain this I must tell you that my flight is endless, being a flight from jealousy. Among the jealous was Icarus himself who, in flight with me, was in flight from me. Those ruled by jealousy

15

accuse. They say I murdered Talos, my sister's son, and they also say that Talos was my equal before he reached manhood. The jealous accuse me of jealousy and say that, being jealous, I killed Talos and fled from Athens to a deme where the people took my name and called themselves Daedalids, thereafter making small and primitive votive horses out of bronze in a manner I taught them. The horses are pleasant, those I have seen, but unambitious and you would think that those who tell this story would credit me with better taught followers – but that is a digression. I accused these people of inexpert stone carving. These people accused me of murder. It was not true but it was believed and Icarus too believed it. From this accusation I fled.

There is much confusion about Talos, my nephew. Firstly, it is said that he invented the potter's wheel and that is true. They also say he found a fish spine and cast it in iron and thus made the iron saw, and that is partially true. He found the bone and recognized that it could be made into a tool, but it was I who cast it. In Crete we have iron saws four feet long and we have others no larger than needles for fine work. These small ones I cast from the legs of grasshoppers, but let that pass. He invented the saw. In the same fish spine, I foresaw the structure of our wings, but let that pass too.

What is to the point is that they say he died in Attica and his soul became a partridge. This nonsense Icarus believed, though he was not born at the time. Talos did not die in Attica but in Crete, long after, where Medea killed him. When he came to Crete he had lost his skill and by a curious chance he lost his skill in the kiln and emerged from it as bronze. Being bronze, he came to Crete and took service with Minos in a capacity suitable to one who had lost his skill and become bronze. Having become bronze and simple he became a military man and the guardian of Crete. It was his habit to throw rocks at passing vessels and to give vent to brazen shouts. As a result of this display, he too became a legend. There were those who said Zeus had made him. There were those who said he sprang from an ash tree and was the last of his race. In one sense this could be said to be true since ash wood gives the great heat necessary to smelting and to that extent he doubtless sprang from an ash tree in his brazen form. Certainly he was the last of his race and this does not disturb me. It has also been said that Hephaistos forged Talos in Sardinia but he was quite evidently cast and not beaten out in bronze. There has been no end to what they say about my nephew Talos, but they do not explain how I could have murdered him in Athens, by throwing him from the Acropolis, when he was manifestly on Crete and in a position of authority, at a later date.

Talos, prudently, said nothing. I saw him often on the shore, among the rocks, with his blank, bronze face and his thick neck. In his neck was a bronze stopper which closed the single vein down which his life ran to his feet – a poor contrivance to hold in a soul. The soul of Talos, such as it was, ran sluggishly up and down this pipe and it was not a partridge but the lost wax of his casting in bronze. It is remarkable how credulous people can be, believing so many opposed things about my nephew. Icarus clung to this notion about the partridge because his aunt was called

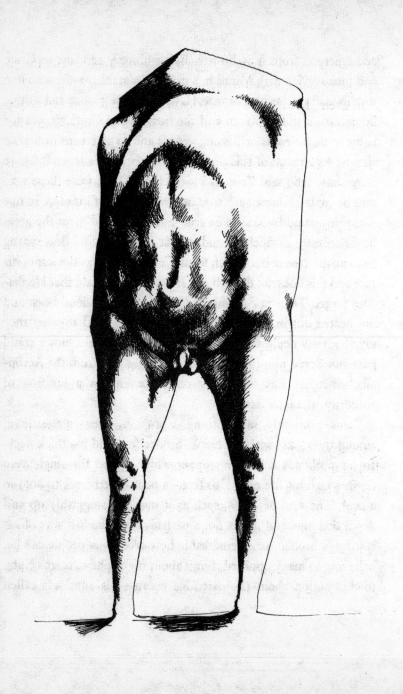

Perdix and also Polycaste, which influenced him. He feared partridges and shunned them.

In Crete, I too was in the service of Minos and there is scarcely anything in the palace at Knossos worth a second glance, for which I have not been given the credit. Minos was priest to Poseidon in the aspect of a bull, so that Minos wore a gold bull mask on ceremonial occasions. I made the mask and people identified Minos with the bull god. He was, however, neither a god nor a bull and this latter deficiency was resented by his queen, Pasiphaë, who became enamoured of a white bull, sacred to Poseidon, which awaited sacrifice. Pasiphaë was given to strange passions. She caused me to construct a cow of hides on a wicker frame, so that the bull would mount her in this travesty. I had no alternative. She was the Queen and priestess of the Mother, but Minos, in jealous fury, blamed me for the adultery of his queen. This is the sort of situation that arises when you possess some unusual skills. I am continually the victim of jealousy in one form or another. It was my invention which enabled Pasiphaë to enjoy the white bull and I admit it, but Minos imputed more to me than carpentry. Icarus, too, believed worse of me and said so, as we lay locked in the Labyrinth whilst I made our wings. On those wings, in flight from the jealousy of Minos, we quitted Crete at the time of the birth of the Minotaur. Ariadne released us and we went out on to the terrace of the palace and stood together on the hot stones at midday, when the palace slept. No one watched us begin our flight but the lizards who lay staring at the flies. The flies evaded them and whined up from the terrace. I remember counting that good. The hawks scouring down the valley were the other living things who saw us.

Knowing nothing of what was in his mind, I warned Icarus of the various risks of flight. Since that time, the story goes that I warned him of the heat of the sun, which stood at his apex, blazing

16. 4. 61.

down on us, but that is wisdom after the event. I never thought of such a chance. I warned him of stress in the dive and to fly smoothly to cover the distance. He smiled, watching the lizards and I heard him say – or thought I heard words turning in his mind. I thought he said:

20

I find myself alone, live, in a golden age
Peopled with monsters of whom I am one
Transformed in sleep and cringing in the cage
Of a new monster born
Winged, in the scorn of the sun.

To the half-bull alone I am half-brother
Horned with bone pinions in the day glare.
Mazed in the dark, groping, another
Horned monster is alive
Alone and lowing despair.

I cannot stay here now . . . clenched predatory on my rage.

I heard these words and understood them in their confusion and pain and I listened to the silence wondering why all this confusion and inconsequence should enwrap my son's mind. Why should he think himself a monster? Why should the birth of the Minotaur concern him in this way? I could see how he blamed me but I could see no way to explain matters simply. Then he said again!

I cannot stay here now, clenched to this stone

and I saw him lift his spread of wings impatiently so that they clattered. His thoughts seemed to twist and writhe in a labyrinth of their own making.

I cannot stay here now, clenched to this stone
In my father's presence, knowing the deep
And nether mouth, the simulacrum grown
        To drop the Minotaur
Stunned still in the maze of sleep.

I seemed golden in my time, neither alone
Nor monstrous in my childhood growing

I could not catch the rest. Icarus looked at me and then he spoke out loud. He said:

In all his time my father could not make
A kestrel's egg. Yet I am born from one
Hatched new into a griffon who can shake
His life into the sea
And spill his seed on the sun.

I realized then that he was determined on a violent course and that what in him was monstrous was his ill-aimed rage and his despair, so that he would not be comforted by words. I said nothing.

  He saw himself, I suppose, as a shadow even then and as shadows are stretched and distorted by the ground they fall on and the angle of the light which casts them, he saw a monstrous shadow thrown upon the terrace. He was a shadow cast by the god and yet a shadow altered and deformed by the overlapping of my shadow and I looked down and saw that it was so. Our shadows were locked together, appearing four-legged and misshapen. This shadow shape, like a winged bull, lay sprawled before me.

He moved to break the image and I looked up and saw him before he turned away. In his eyes I saw that he believed a coil of desperate falsehoods. He believed I had murdered Talos. He believed I had fathered the Minotaur on Pasiphaë and he thought himself half-brother to a monster and cousin to the ghost of Talos, in the form of a partridge. When a man believes such a tangle as that, there are no words to be said. Even his father is silenced.

I suppose I knew that his rejection of me was natural and I accepted it, grieving. It was the shadow of my fame which cloaked Icarus and the fragments, which are gathered haphazard in the basket of my reputation, were clicking in his mind like knucklebones. I saw the crest of his shoulders rise and his back took up the tension of his wings. He breathed quickly and heavily. His thighs stretched to take up the pull and they were grooved with the power building in him to thrust. Then he turned back towards me and looked up into the sun, grinning. I have seen such a grimace worn by soldiers driving themselves to courage, facing the spears opposed to them.

Then he left me and went into the sky, taking the rising hot wind, upswinging from the valley, as I had taught him. He flew into the air, swooping downwards towards the sea to gain momentum. The wind took him and threw him up on the current and he held himself rigid, stretched like a bat, like the bats whose flight I had studied in the long night in the Labyrinth, whilst I made the wings.

In that moment I was caught myself, in a whirlpool of half-born thoughts. I stood watching Icarus climb, watching the results of my calculation, watching him take advantage of the wind as I had taught him, spill air and take it again, hot from below him, beating upwards with long strokes and I triumphed in the knowledge that

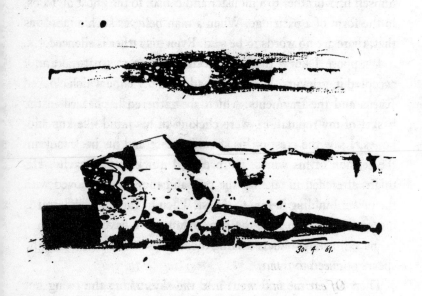

30. 4. 61.

I had contrived this possibility of flight. Yet I knew, as I watched him swim in his new dimension, that I had destroyed my own son. With part of my mind I tried to assemble the crumbling half-formed pieces of his thought. But he evaded me and slid away into his ambition and I lost him.

24

I waited, I do not know for what. I hoped to hear him speak again, and later, as you will hear, I heard some pieces of his dream. They fell from him as he held his height and rose far above me, for I was never near him again on our flight.

I knew then how it would end and I understood and accepted that Icarus had gone to battle with his high love and adversary and that this was the time of Icarus and his glory.

It was not I who had cast Icarus into shadow, making his shadow monstrous. I had merely stepped between him and the sun for a moment – the moment that separated him from childhood and the achievement of death.

I raised my wings and followed him into the sky. I came up over the port and went out over the calm sea, below Icarus and far behind him. Dropping down from far above me his vain triumph drifted in the wind and I caught it on its way. He sang and shouted defiance at the sun and at mankind in these words:

> *All men are lizards trapped by time in dust*
> *To scuffle in it with their crumpled hands.*
> *They write their lives by marking on the crust*
> *Of earthbound time, their symbols in the sands.*
> *Dirt is their cluttered kingdom where they grind*
> *The harvest of the years, sloughing their sheaths,*
> *Scraping their paper off to free their kind*
> *From mortal limitations. He who breathes*
> *Only the sallow lees of midday in*
> *Lies splayed upon this midden where the flies*

Tease him and whine and spurn the blinded grin
He wears to watch them spinning as they rise.

I also was a lizard prisoned, caught,
Who now am bird and hold my high-born state
In feathered fury, I was reptile-wrought,
Who now look down on reptiles. Yet they wait
In polished quiet and seek to stare down time.
Hoping the god will throw me from the skies.
You lizards were my gaolers, you were lime
To take ambition, fork-tongued, by surprise
And gulp it out of mind. Those shining stones
You bleakly stare with, give you sleepless sight
To stare down time by side-sight, yet your bones
Are hammered to the rock in want of flight.

He went wheeling and tumbling about the sky as if born in it, shouting defiance and fooling no one. A hawk, curiously far out over the sea, veered away and plunged towards the land behind us.

You canting kestrel streaming down the sky
Plummet and screaming quit your cherished height
In anguish. Oh Apollo, lidless eye
Who gives all sight to creatures, mark her plight
And smile upon her passage as you fill
The bowl of morning with your gilded spite.
Go, stalk your apex, yawning as you spill

Your phoenix gold upon her and your might.
Lean on her back and drive her down the sky
Weigh down her wings with all your weight of light.
I come to match you. Icarus can fly
To combat with a burning god in flight.

Icarus flies to tear the furnace wind,
Climbs the steep sky to hawk the lowering sun
And tread upon his malice. I am finned
To swim the flooding sun-shoal in my run.
My scream shall cause the molten sky to shake:
Fall, kestrel, from your haven in the wind,
You lizard bird who tumble in my wake,
Fall as you scream and splinter up your scream
And seek the shadow's comfort and the lake
Of darkness under mountains. In the stream
Of hungry heat the god pours out, I take
The source of my ascent towards my dream.

And so upwards. The hot wind rising took Icarus high and higher. He looked like a double-axe suspended, diminishing until I lost sight of him, seeing or sensing him in the eye of the sun as a black spot, until, blinded, I could no longer look for him. The hours passed and Apollo, disdaining his strutting adversary, went quietly down towards the rim of the sea, in his accustomed fashion. The sun goes down into the sea every day, in spite of any challenge. Evening came on, as you might expect. We were seven hours out from Crete, I suppose, by that time and as the light thickened I heard a final verse from the Song of the Triumph of Icarus – if that is what it could be called.

> *Poor lizard, stiffened in the lichen scrawl,*
> *Making your nervous shelter in the night,*
> *Watching the kestrel shadow on the wall*
> *Knit up the day and stitch the dying light*
> *Upon the evening. Day dies in the grass;*
> *Eat it then, lizard, make this day your own.*
> *The kestrel cinder in the burning glass*
> *Is stooped in twilight. Icarus alone*
> *Towers in the milk of mist shrouding his prey*
> *And wheels across the shadow of the net*
> *Which snares the broken fragments of the day*
> *Where I have conquered and the sun is set.*

Such arrogance is breath-taking. Who did he think he had conquered? All the days he had lived, he had seen end like this one and what battle had been fought? To keep up one's spirits with bragging is well enough when night comes on, but to imagine oneself responsible for the normal circle of day into night is a remarkable imaginative feat.

I do not think, looking back, that Icarus had any very clear idea of reality and perhaps this ignorance served him in his final gesture, for in that, he went out of reality in a fashion which I did not and do not understand. But we shall presently come to that. For the moment I must tell you more about him and the various signs he gave me of what he would become. I should have had a deeper foreknowledge of his fate. At least I had been given a great many clues as to the nature of my son.

When Icarus was a child, I gave him the shell of a chambered nautilus. It was a grave and harmonious thing, curved to a perfection beyond the ram's horn and Icarus took it and held it to his

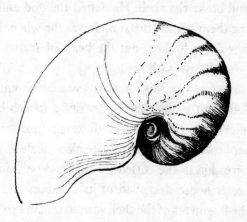

ear, to listen to the sea. I told him then that perfection dwelt in the spiral of that shell and all harmony was governed by the law of number and by a divine geometry which could be seen in the structure of the nautilus and Icarus laughed to hear the sea move in the shell. I told him that all things were measured and dwelt in proportion and he continued to listen to the sound of the sea. He did not look at the shell cupped in his child's hands and even then I should have known him better. Then I told him that the gods contrived their playthings in accordance with laws which even they did not understand. Making these things, they yet knew nothing of proportion. But Icarus listened only to the breathing of the shell of Nautilus. Presently he broke it because he was clumsy with his hands. From that time on Icarus had no sense of proportion. I did not know this, but it was there to be seen. He broke the shell to find its golden centre, to find the sea hidden in its heart. He broke it impatiently because he was clumsy with his hands. He defied me and broke the shell. He defied the god and broke my wings, testing them against the sun. It was the wings I made that the sun threw down broken, but the heart of Icarus broke first, because he was clumsy with his love.

I should have foreseen this for Icarus was consistent in his love and in his folly, but at the time I only saw a foolish boy break a seashell. I picked up the slim and glittering fragments and saw each chamber broken open, each private place made blankly public and the progression to the curled tip smashed out of its context. I saw the secret house despoiled of its darkness and seeing my hands and the fragments of the shell scattered in my palms, I wondered, not so much that Icarus had broken the nautilus, but why I, with all my skill, could never mend it.

Naucrate was a slave, the property of Minos and she was my wife and the mother of Icarus. She was of the sea and it may be that Icarus heard his mother's voice in the nautilus shell, whispering. She was loved by Pasiphaë, the queen, who was given to many forms of love. Pasiphaë, being priestess to the Mother, was of the night and of the moon and of rain and Icarus feared her. He had a great fear of the night. This you may think curious since his name dedicates him to the moon and perhaps it was Pasiphaë who moved in this. Given to the moon by his mother, whom Pasiphaë loved, perhaps it was not surprising that Icarus should have sought to destroy the sun, whom he loved. Or perhaps his life fell between his clumsy loves and broke upon his hard and fierce defiance.

Children often fear the night but when he was a child, Icarus feared the night more painfully than other children. His fear of the moon could not be overcome. He identified Pasiphaë with the moon and hated his own name. When she had coupled with the white bull and borne the Minotaur, he felt a kinship with the creature and a shame in this. But all his life, before that time, he hated Pasiphaë for love of Naucrate and the moon for love of the sun. His mother was of the sea and in due time he returned to the sea.

Without Pasiphaë there would have been no flight from Crete, no simulacrum of a dappled cow and no Minotaur in the centre of the Labyrinth where in darkness and bewilderment, that bull-headed half-god, who was no man and no natural son, lowed out his lonely singularity. In the outer chamber of this earth-turned nautilus, this labyrinth I had made, Icarus and I were locked by Minos, in his jealousy. The subjects of Minos concern themselves with bulls to an unnatural extent, but this is not surprising. Their king thinks himself a bull. All that they have to fear on Crete, for they have no rivals and no enemies, is the bull who is Poseidon, who lives beneath the earth and whose furious tramplings bring down walls and break the rocks. I myself am in some doubt about

31

the existence of this bull under the ground, but on Crete everything is attributed to the behaviour of bulls, and this simplifies matters. Certainly this much was true. Minos, of the line of

Minos the bull king, brought me to the crisis and Poseidon, in the guise of a bull, was the accidental author of my flight.

Do you see order in all this, if not harmony? A king, masked like a bull, his horns gilded, becomes cuckold to a sacred bull and wears horns for a god. A woman, queen and image of the moon, lies with a bull at night and bears a bull-headed god-beast who must live in the centre of night, within a maze, divorced even from moonlight. Pasiphaë began it. Icarus gained his victory from it and I was its victim. In all this I see an order which I could no more change than mend the broken shell of Nautilus, the ordered labyrinth of the sea in little.

These things Icarus too perceived after a fashion, but, lacking a sense of proportion, he misjudged them. Dimly he saw a labyrinth of circumstances which made up his life and blundered about in it, seeking a proper shape. He feared the night which turns inward towards its centre. He feared the sun's measured passage across the sky and hated the god's descent into the sea, which brought him daily to the labyrinth of darkness. Loving the god more than he feared him, loving day at the expense of night, loving the part seen and in hatred of the part unseen, he could not comprehend the circle he saw round him. These are among the reasons for his audacious and disastrous act. He sought to stay the sun's journey. He sought to destroy the order of the god's passage, because he feared the measurement of action, knowing nothing of the consequence of action. This failure of perception brought him to death. He went into the night forever, in defiance of it. He hated order, yet loved the sun, who, among gods, approaches nearest in his behaviour to an ordered harmony. He loved the god in a most disordered fashion.

I myself know that I did not perceive these things clearly at that time. Perhaps I should have seen more in the breaking of the shell

33

than I did – or perhaps I now read too much into this episode. Icarus was only a child then. What he feared he defied. What he loved he challenged. He accepted nothing and this is heroic. I remain baffled by heroes. The fact that we did not understand one another, Icarus and I, is due to my being a most ordered man or ultimately an insensitive one. It is not simple. There is a kind of stupidity buried in intelligence.

We had flown north through half the day, Icarus rising. I followed him, taking the wind and holding my place below him without difficulty. In the evening, as the sun turned down into the sea I heard Icarus shout the last of his empty challenge and it seemed to drop and dwindle in the sun's wake down towards the edge of the sea. The god ignored him and moved downwards, as the night came up. Cloud gathered, dredged from the sea and filled with fears.

I looked down and the sea was beaten and scuffed with breakers. It was leaden and yet ruffled. It was like a dancing floor disturbed by the feet of dancers who had forgotten their steps. Icarus cried out, complaining and questioning. I heard him clearly and his words fell like pieces of metal.

> *Cold, cold and swaddling cloud*
> *Humped on the pitch of sea,*
> *On the pitch and cobalt cold*
> *You cumulus encroaching.*
> *Is it for this bleak skyscape ploughed*
> *By the furrowing moon*

I hang, on the neck of night,
On the shifting sky?
Is it for this, close hauled, alone,
I count my minutes down?

Only the hoplite gull
And gorging cormorant
Haunt here and inhabit
The salt sky, searching.
Is it the sea wheel held in the pull
Of the sprocket moon
I watch with the steering gull
On her combing climb?
Is it for this the light is gone
And the vault is cold as stone?

In all a god's life length
There has been no man here
To fly on ricket wings
Nor ambition outreaching
The coil and stretch of my strength.
Does the languid moon
Hold me hung in her net
As she drags the sea?
Is it for this white weary throne
That I was winged and grown?

The dancing floor darkened and vanished. It was gone like the dancing floor I had made for Ariadne, like the dancing floors of Crete. Crete was in my mind and the loss of it. I remembered watching my pupils Dipoinos and Skyllis carving stone. They were not adept. I remembered Naucrate. Icarus, sharing my thoughts, or I his, spoke of Crete where he had lived before we fled from it.

> No longer long-tongued Crete
> Loafs in the crawl of shallows,
> Warm in the trawl of time.
> Is it the loss of islands keeping
> Their slim and seal-backed fleet
> Or the draining moon
> Sucking my life in the night
> I mourn in the wound?
> Is it for Crete like a broken bone
> Sunk in the sea and gone?
>
> There will not be a night
> To come to me again
> In my flight and combat quest
> In the day returning
> Here on my patch of brief held height
> By the summit moon
> I wait my death ahead
> My proper ending.

> *It is for this, close-hauled, alone,*
> *I count my minutes down.*

Less rhetoric, less pomp, less defiance. Yet I did not believe Icarus would abandon his *hubris* or would pray the god to spare him and would come down and fly on with me in proper humility. He expected a god to wake and come out of the night to give him battle.

He expected to alter a god's ordained passage across the sky from dawn to dusk and dusk to dawn. A boy dressed as a bird – did he think himself a target for Apollo's arrows – a coxcomb in cocks' plumage?

I suppose if it had meant nothing to me, if I had been a bystander, I should have laughed. To anyone else it would have been comic. He did not come down nor speak directly to me but when I heard the last verse of his song and he spoke of his proper ending I knew he would not alter in his determination. Perhaps the shell of Nautilus was the key. The night looked like a hollow shell.

In the nautilus of night there are many nights each in proportion smaller than the last; each has its measured room. But the last, curled in the very centre of the shell, is a night forever closed against the morning. There is the trap and end of night in the shell which cannot be broken. In that small and final chamber, wrapped like a foetus, is the night to come. For Icarus the centre of the shell hung between sea and sky. I could not see him because he was high above and it was the darkest time of night, the deep cold time when the god's breath no longer warms the air.

We flew on, in our flight from Crete, invisible to one another. The god had gone down, and into his holy hide below the sea rim. Crete was far behind us and I, the first man to have seen the full shape of that island in its ocean bed, would not see it again.

In your time, others flying in predatory flocks will look down and see the shape of Crete as I have done but with foreknowledge. They will fall upon the island carefully. They will fly fast and come to kill, hunting the sky, and the earth will be their quarry. Perhaps there will even be a time when their wings, shining in the sun, will fly without men and the hunters will sit in hides elsewhere looking not at the island but only at the charted shape of it. None of this will be to avenge me nor will they think of me; nor learn anything from me except my skills and a few facts.

I learned many things on that flight. I learned the exact shapes and the boundaries of islands set in the sea, for I could see them entire. I saw the pale shallows and the mottled darkness of the deeps and I saw how islands chanced above the surface and where, but for a fathom or so, there would have been other islands. In this there was some disorder and lack of sequence, for the sea bed, cooled in its flow like bronze in the mould, had not been poured with reasonable and consequential care into its shape, although the covering water dressed it like a *chlamys*. But this I saw, now that I think back, before the moon set. Icarus I did not see. The moon had been chill and sour, like an unripe grape. The bunched clouds pulsed and moved as if they could not sleep. If she saw Icarus, what would the moon have cared that he hated her? I thought of Naucrate who gave Icarus to the moon at his birth and wondered at a gift so ill directed. Naucrate was of the sea. Her name means 'sea power'. She was Greek, not Cretan. Although Icarus hated the moon, he had no fear of the sea which was his mother's place. For this reason, although I had warned him of the sea so that he should not fly too low and let the breakers catch his pinions, he thought nothing of this contingency. I told him, high and breaking waves could drag him down out of the air, but he took no notice, knowing perhaps that the sea would have his wings soon enough and without effort.

When I look back on this event and remember how I hung there in the wind and beat north and west, never seeming to move, I remember that I wondered then, as I do now, how certain Icarus had been of his life's climax all his life. Sometimes it seems to me that in all his life he had no purpose until he came to the days of his flight. He had no interest in my crafts, no interest in bronze casting or in the skills which lie in the fingers, nor did he care for the ways in which useful things can be properly and cun-

ningly made. He was in no way concerned with the devious and interesting ways in which power can be gained and made to serve an end. He lived suspended. There was neither gravity in him nor laughter. His eyes, I remembered, were those of a man already gone.

It must be that his purpose was fused to the sun and had been, long before I ever knew of it and that he dreamed of a conquest he knew he would never achieve. Or did he think he could pull down Apollo? Poets and prophets being madmen are all unmanageable forces, lacking utility and kindness. Their reality cuts like a knife. When Dionysus wounds, his wine is blood.

I myself am descended from gods and kings but I do not much concern myself with the fact, unless it can be useful. I am not insensitive to the visions of poets and other sacred persons but in general they are less observant than they think, suffering as they do from revelation, which blinds them. I am not unaware of the value of poetic vision and I accept, I suppose, that what poets celebrate are important things, such as honour and beauty and birth and valour and man's relation to the gods and who they are and their history and so on. I am also aware of the world and of its appearance and its consequence, and I suspect that, since deduction and experiment have been my methods of gaining experience, I am no worse off and better instructed in these matters than many poets. Certainly I am better off than any hero, since I am not beset by my own personality. Cognition I prefer to revelation and in my view the valiant act is to live as long as possible, but then I am a maker of things and that takes time. Honour lasts longer if it is gained by patient discovery rather than by brief nobility of action, or so it has always seemed to me. I am involved in an art and do not wish to be interrupted nor pressed beyond my proper pace by eloquent activities, the caprice of gods, immeasurable speculation nor any apotheosis. What I make exists.

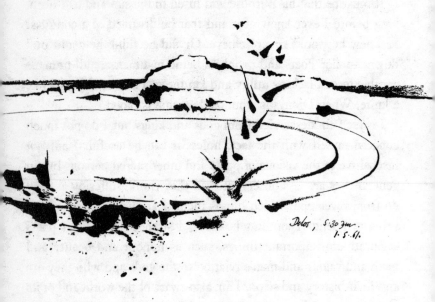

Delos, 5.30 ʒm.
1. 5. 61.

With such thoughts I concerned myself as I flew. I was not comforted although I believe what I have said. The moon sank and light stained upwards from the horizon in preparation for the rising god who had circled the defeated night and came up behind me, spattered with new blood. I looked for Icarus and could not see him, nor did I see him. I looked down and saw below me the sacred island, Delos, the sanctuary of the god's mother, where Apollo was born, the island which once floated invisible and now was anchored to the sea bed.

What I make exists. What Icarus would make that day does not exist but there is no need for him to do more. Looking down on Delos as the island waked, passing from silver into the god's gold, I wondered and became unsure of the virtues of my calling and the skills of which I was master. Although I am a technician I am perfectly capable of drunkenness and am grateful in some ways for the leopard of Dionysus when he nuzzles at my brain. It was such a time, and the god came into me. I take it Dionysus was the god, although I had drunk nothing. It could hardly have been Apollo himself for I could see him rising. You never know precisely when and how you are possessed but I think my promptings came from Dionysus.

The air seemed to shake and I fell. I fell several hundred feet before a hot gust bore me up again. The island shone. I swung over it, caught in a combat of currents in the air. All swayed and rippled. From Delos, Aphrodite's doves flew up and scattered like paper torn and thrown into the air. That morning was a great and simple joy and Icarus shouted and sang of it:

> See the earth sparkles, glittering gives ground
> And rises gasping from the birth of day
> So that the lion hills that lift their round
> And bossy brows beneath the helmet heat

43

Shake as the armoured morning leaps to greet
Their ancient harness and their crests of clay.

Now the sky shouts. It treads upon the strand
And spills upon the pelvis of the beach
So that the sea slides downwards from the sand
Spread wide and waiting in the shift of surf.
The shingle moves and scatters on the turf
The glutton tide strives urgently to reach.

Time has the scent of thyme, the dove starts up
And claps her fluting wings against the vault
So that with slapping clatter in the cup
Of morning, Time is feathered as it turns:
The minutes flicker and the morning burns
To lie like jetsam in the rime of salt.

The dry stream under Kynthos wakes from sleep
Where the dry lakes lie tousled from their drought
So that the very rocks which held the deep
And ancient womb of summer loose their grip,
Give up the summer god and let him slip
To rock the radiant island with his shout.

There is no death, there is no death nor birth:
There is no present birth nor fruiting thing
So that the shrill and stridulated mirth

The mocking beetle breeds in shifting dust
Is trickled in a travesty of lust
To fall like liquid in the dust-choked spring.

See, where the sea is taken in her bed
And grasps the sun in climax on her shore
So that the breathing shingle at her head
Stirs with her passion, ridden by the god,
Who tips the burning chalice through the rod
And pours his milk into her sucking core.

The sun, my waiting death, raises his eye
And glances from his mating at my flight
So that my shadow slants and seems to die
And crumples like a seabird on the stones
With tattered feathers spread on splintered bones
Trapped in the crystal prison of his sight.

Here over Delos is my tip of time:
Over his golden birthplace is the clash
So that the coming summit of my climb
Will mark the sudden dying of my day.
Here will my wings weep wax and burn away
And all my plumage crumble into ash.

I who have held the element of space
Within a man-made span disdaining fear

So that the strutting dove shied from her place
And fluttered frightened while I hawked the sun:
I, who am Icarus, whose life is gone
Cry my defiance in the sungod's ear.

The sungod rises from the weary sea
Where she lies slack with surfeit in her bed
So that the rising god looks up at me
Smiling upon his hearth of summer sky
Measures his realm and floods it with his eye
And leaves the sea, to take me in her stead.

See, the sky darkens; glittering he drowns
My fear of dying. I have made my run
So that the very top and height that crowns
My trajectory, holds me in it still
Apollo my beloved, by my will
I hold you coupled and possess the sun.

Poor Icarus, poor bird-scarer bird. Kestrel and dove fly from you, whilst you fly from a partridge. Is it that small perfection flies from the splendour of a great fault and a great fault fears small perfections? Are there elements in hope and hatred which will not fuse with proper metals? There is no philosophy to be whittled out of flight, to be shaped and polished from the whittled down perfected flight of creatures born to fly. No owl flies near you, Icarus, nor any wisdom. No bird stares at the sun. No bird courts death.

No bird watches its splayed shadow on the beach nor the shadows of its fledglings, strung on lath and feathers. Man watches little else. His fearful shadow is his fear.

It was midday when I climbed away from Delos and the sacred place fell away. Paros passed below me and Naxos. These islands swam together and were lost, brooding in the swallowing sea.

There is much patience to be gained from foreknowledge and this, I surmise, Icarus had. He knew his death and waited on it and he made continual boasts about his way of dying and cried defiance into the top of the sky. I could not hear him clearly. I do not know where he was at that time, but he was high, higher than my wings could have carried a normal man. I had not designed them for the purpose he put them to and do not know how he made them carry him so high. He made more of his wings than I can understand. Presently I shall try to explain what I think must have happened.

To make a thing is to touch dead things and breathe on them. Stone, wood, metals, the fierce and valiant bronze, are dead until I take them up. Bronze lies in parts, in brittle copper, and grey tin until I fuse them in proper proportion. There is no bronze without these proper proportions and no wings made without knowledge of stress and curve. Icarus, having no proper craft, could only breathe upon and touch his own life. He breathed death into his life to bring himself alive and in this making, breathed upon the wings that I had made. The result continues to astonish me. I do not know what transformation he achieved for although the wings were well contrived they were not suitable for the heights to which he drove them. I cannot see how he managed his climb. Somehow he transformed his wings in flight and he transformed himself. A balk of timber, catgut, eagle feathers, wax, wire, all these things need craft to use them properly for wings. And Icarus himself, a stone uncut, ores unalloyed, a wax, a malleable stuff, what skill did he have to make of himself what he made? He was not a maker of things, he could not touch dead things and make them live. Yet he touched himself alive with death and this was his creation. This reversal of the proper order must possess its own logic. It is as if he went upwards into the kiln as bronze, wrapped in the mould of his wings, as if he poured upwards and emerged as Icarus in a new metal. The god was his kiln. Somewhere there was a random factor. I, Daedalus, maker, never before or since saw a man make himself from nothing. This thing I had never known, although I make my own magic from common clay. A little after midday, beyond Delos, my son came back into my sight from beyond the sky and I must try to describe what I saw, if I saw it. I am not sure even of this, but I experienced the apex of the flight of Icarus although I did not, could not, have seen it. I do not see how I could have seen it.

At his tip of time, at his apex, he moved upon the sun and joined the god. At this summit, his moving mass changed its form. His trunk splayed outwards, expanding, and the jointed projections of his limbs, disordered in the fission of his body, became the vectors of an energy beyond mortal strength. His proportions altered and his structure was transformed. The cage of ribs passed through the ribs of wing, each performing an identical function, affirming the ascent implicit in the descent. The wings of his pelvis spread

48

from the spine and in their bowl the duration of his flight was contained like a liquid. At maximum velocity, the sequence of modifications, to which Icarus was subject, appeared simultaneous. A compact projectile and yet spread across the sky, he evolved in that instant a sequence of related anatomies, each designed to succeed and doomed to fail. In these anatomies, the embryo coexisted with the fish, the lizard with the bird and the disintegration of ultimate fatigue moved with the impulse towards birth.

As I watched, the geometry of his fall demonstrated the ratio of victory to defeat in the mirror of his rise. The action and contraction of the form I had identified with Icarus rested upon the summit of strain in total repose. A disunity, a chance factor, seemed to shift the emphasis from his humanity and place it on the order of his flight. The shape of flight itself embraced him and his humanity took on another shape. It was not of the order of my own.

I saw this happen, yet how could I have seen it? There was no sound, but a heat so powerful that it rang in me. The god made no sound but threw Icarus aside from him and in that moment my son cried out. I could not hear him scream. I did not hear it but saw it and it was not a scream of pain but a dreadful cry of loss. It scored the side of space like an ostracon scratched on a shard. It was a splinter narrow as a wire and by it the air was grooved against its nature. The scream fell like a stone, spinning and oscillating. In it, stuck like flies in amber, were words:

> *Give me my god*
> *Give me my burning god.*

The god is lost
I cannot hear him shout
Here in the dark.
I cannot see his face.
His features burn
His head a honeycomb
Burns in the maze
Behind my glued and crippled limping eyes.

See how my eyes are shards
And I am blind.
The god is lost behind my shattered sight
A brazen broken error strikes at me
Whimpers and strikes the silence from the dark
And mocks my cry of flight.

Give him to me
Give me my burning god.

The god is lost
I cannot find my hands
And I am blind.
I cannot find my home
In this deep pit
This cindered honeycomb.
Burnt out and gone,
His image is burnt out. The god is gone.

Where only blackness is
Where blackness is.
I cannot find my way towards the god
He slips me in this pitted labyrinth
So that I cannot touch nor feel his touch
Nor make him fly the night.

The god is lost
The god himself is lost
The god is gone
The god himself is gone.

The air swayed and fell slack and suddenly was restrung like a lyre. In that moment I saw Icarus come out of the sky, turning slowly and capriciously. He seemed at infinite leisure, wandering in sleep down the sky in a gently turning pinwheel and he was wrapped in a pall of smoke which seemed to muffle him against the cold of his journey out of heat.

Although his fall outpaced his rise, it seemed that a lifetime occupied his fall. Time which brings disorder seemed to fall sick and a disorder beyond time inverted that gradual disorder the passage of time creates. Icarus himself was the random factor, the conqueror of order, and in this lay the energy which took him into battle with the sun. From the god himself he stole a particle of that divine energy which holds the sun himself above the sky.

In the time it took for Icarus to fall I seemed to look back into his life. I saw him as a child play with a spider and the spider lead him down the corridors of his own labyrinth, paying into his hand a single thread of silk. There was no part of his life in which he laid aside that thread, no time when he did not follow the spider into the maze, but he did not have the silk tied at the entrance to guide him out into old age. Arachne led him towards the centre, towards the Minotaur, and he followed, expecting to find out who he was in that meeting.

I do not think that meeting took place. I do not know why the name Arachne came to me so clearly. Ariadne was the daughter of Pasiphaë which may have had something to do with it and she helped release us from the labyrinth on Crete, but the names Arachne and Ariadne are not so much alike. I do not see any clear connection, but Icarus seemed to drop down the sky on a long and sticky strand of time, like a spider dropping from a twig. I remember I made a dancing floor for Ariadne.

I heard the Minotaur butt his woolly front against his prison walls and bellow out questions. When he did this the city shook and cracks opened in the earth. The bull beneath the earth thereby became a reality. Icarus called him 'brother' but I had nothing directly to do with the conception of the Minotaur, which was the result of Pasiphaë's appetites. It was not my doing. There was a bronze partridge, but alive, in his hand and Icarus took from its throat a little pin and a cry bubbled and flowed over his fingers. This, I assume, had something to do with Talos. There was a white bull, whose gilded horns were spread like wings and who rose out of the sea, and other things which do not seem to me, looking back, to have precise meaning. All this time, Icarus fell quietly down the long strand of his heroic death.

It has been said that I saw him fall into the sea but I did not. It has also been said that I searched the sea for him and found his body. I searched but I never found him. I do not know what his body became since I did not find him. I remember though what I saw it become before it fell. I found nothing but some fragments of his wings and I took these with me to Cumae and did not bury them on the island which came to be called Icaria, for that island lay far off my course.

They say that Heracles found Icarus; but then they say so many things. There is also a story that in gratitude I made a carving in wood of Heracles. I certainly made such an image but in another place and for quite different reasons. It was at Pisa. Taking my image for a rival, Heracles smashed it with a stone, which was very typical of him. A craftsman has to put up with the behaviour of such demi-gods. They are destructive and make nothing but legends. The story about Heracles finding the body of Icarus is just a tale and there are many such tales, few of them accurate. As for the story of Icarus, it is short and unusually complete in its common form.

I flew on to Cumae when my son died, and as I flew I became uncertain of myself. This I had not been before, since I had not been concerned with myself except in contriving matters. I had been troubled that Icarus did not love me and now it troubled me that his pretensions, which had seemed to me absurd, should seem to form so complete and ordered a pattern. He was a hero and these people I distrust and avoid, but to be a hero one must conquer death. That is the sole function of heroes. I think that Icarus conquered death. Who does not in one way or another? His name at least has conquered the death of years and that is a resounding conquest. I think at the last he conquered himself too and his defeat was his victory, but even so I was disturbed by the shape of his life and death.

I was not sure of his death. I knew him dead and burned and yet I could not think him dead. I felt too that in some way, falling out of the sky, he had returned to me and come to love me and I could find no sensible reason why this should be. All this seemed to me disturbing and fragmentary, part of the shapelessness which often mars the heroic form, yet I could not find the missing element and the sea gave nothing of Icarus back except some burnt fragments of his wings. My thoughts did not come clearly and I flew on feeling only unease and no pain. I turned north towards Attica and at this time two fears grew in me. They were a fear of the god and a fear of myself. In my mind Delos shone. I remembered the story of the god's birth and of his mother Leto who searched the mountains and the islands for a place to give him birth and how all these places feared to harbour the birthplace of an unforgiving god and feared to receive his mother. Delos had quaked in terror during the nine days of the god's deliverance from his mother as she clutched the palm tree in her labour and then the god rose from her and took his lyre and the bow and turned the foundations of the island to gold. This is an old tale and I do not put much faith in such legends. Divinity cloaks itself in fables. Nevertheless, the god is evidently golden. That can be seen. The rest may be true.

Icarus had fallen. I had seen it. When would the sense of loss come upon me? I feared that I did not feel it and so began to fear myself and fear an incomplete and disrupted order in my being. There is no fear to compare with that fear.

Terror is not measurable and is to be despised, yet I was filled with terror. I feared the god although I do not believe gods to be much concerned with the affairs of men. Gods are not concerned with feckless and fragile creatures like my son Icarus, although he did not believe it. He gave everything his own attributes, being mortal in his pride.

I am familiar with intractable materials and with the control of fire, and have some mastery of the inanimate, knowing how to use things with precision and employ their power. I doubt if gods, who lack precision and need no power but their own, are born on little quaking islands or care much for men's praise or fear. Gods, I suspect, are matter of a different order of energy and need no birthplace but space. However, I may be wrong and I feared the god for myself, as the father of Icarus, not being a hero. Apollo has greater precision than other gods and my fear grew.

There is a long list of the god's victims. Tityos was the first and then Python, who guarded the navel of the world, and thereafter a great many more. It is a dull catalogue of casualties. On the other hand, should the god leave or fail to move upwards with the morning, all living things would be his victims. Therefore, he must have mercy on the world or take no interest in it. It is not logical that a god should be selective, therefore I think he is not concerned with victims. He is unforgiving, not knowing forgiveness. He is not interested. And I? Was I a god that I could feel nothing of my loss?

To become a myth a man must complete a pattern and this Icarus had not yet done. He fell blinded out of the sun and I could not find him. I could not then find the form and significance of his actions and so I could not believe in him. Perhaps there was some truth tucked into this sophistry. With it I tried to explain myself, hoping for grief, and I invoked the god, asking in justice for pain. He sent me no sign. It was not, after all, his eclipse.

I flew on northwards and towards the west, weary of searching and weary of flight. It was in the night which followed that Icarus spoke from the sea. My wings were heavy and I dropped towards the sea, flying short of breath and pressed down by the weight of the sky. It was a calm night and the sea swell heaved and subsided as if Poseidon breathed deeply in his sleep. As I flew near to the southern tip of Attica, Icarus murmured in the pull of the sea, his voice rising and falling gently. He spoke as if he had been claimed by the sea many years before:

> *There is a harpy thought caught in my quiet*
> *The depths are not my evil, nor the flood*
> *Where the blind sea moves searching my blind eyes*
> *For proof of death. I do not move but move*
> *Being long dead and drowned in her clear blood.*
>
> *No element divides the silences*
> *The muffled sea robes this my tidal bed;*

The salt and fretted foams are now my skies
The air I breathe, unbreathing, is the sea
That restless stirs beneath my restless head.

No ruffled sweat of mist disturbs my calm
Nor is the wrack my peril, nor the reef.
The fisher sighting at the heavens, sighs
And blends into the sighing wind his song
To merge into the spume of ancient grief.

Long winter solstice of the drunken deeps
Is my long interim, my sharp-sprung trap
Wherein the sea beats, swelling on the rise
Of autumn in the shuttle rocking winds
Which spill sick summer into winter's lap.

And yet I am not quiet who makes no sound;
A fury rides my rest and holds me yet
Clawing the lethargy behind my eyes
And crouching on my shattered nautilus.
I am not dead whose heart is still beset.

Though I am dead and drowned I am not done
For I am strung upon a jointed lie
Of thought-hinged hopes whereon no stranger dies
Nor finds the death he seeks, nor any death,
Yet still is dead, who cannot hope to die.

Nothing is here, nothing that I would have,
After my tempest rise and torrent fall.
Nothing is here to know, nor is the prize
Of death a knowledge nor a resting place;
There is no taste to death, not even gall.

Oh damned drowned death, my net, my leaded line
Which is not sleep nor any sum of sleeps;
The fishing seabird spearing my disguise
Plucks at my hope to feed her yawning want;
The sea is harvested and still she reaps.

I will not die, I will not drown and die
Though I am drowned and dead, I am not done.
Time curves across the arch and where it ties
The slender strands of seasons, there is death
Who knots them into mesh and makes them one.

Therefore I dream and turn upon my dream
And spiral altered upwards to the sky.
I who was fish and lizard yet can prize
The kestrel flying future loose from death,
For Icarus there is no death to die.

Yet I am blind, who feared the shroud of dark
And I am blackened ash who loved the light,
Who sought to love the sun and still defies

The deep sea darkness, holding to my love.
What death is there for me who died in flight?

After that I heard no more and there is no more to tell. I flew on, hoping for some sign that the god forgave Icarus and yet I was unconvinced, for, as I have said, I see no reason why gods should concern themselves with such things. Yet being an ordinary man I was afraid, at once contemptuous of my fear and seeking a way out of it. I flew near the god's special places, sweeping low over Delphi, although it was far off my course, but the sun shone blandly and I felt nothing. There was no sign.

I am not versed in the niceties of religion and although I know useful charms for making metals alloy and cleansing the faults from unhewn stone, I do not know quite what is proper to placate the restless ghost of Icarus and give him peace, nor how to propitiate the god in circumstances so irregular as those I have witnessed. I am not a priest. That function image makers once had, but it is lost to them. I did not consult the oracle at Delphi; I am not at ease with such mystics. I flew on towards Italy.

Icarus has not spoken again. Perhaps the god accepts his burnt offering and he will be content. I am perplexed. I cannot come to terms with the Sky Gods, perhaps because what I make is made from earth, so that the worship of the Mother comes more naturally to me than the politics of Olympus. In any case, I have paid scant attention to devotion of any formal sort for many years. I have been busy and much of my business is in the name of one god or another. Pasiphaë has something to do with all that has occurred but I am not quite sure what. The devotion of Icarus to the sky perhaps offended her.

The sky now fills me with fear and I shall not fly again. Others will do so and I shall call them Icarus. I rest now at Cumae below the Acropolis. Even this rock is crowned with Apollo's temple and the Mother surely sits in the cavern beneath it, deep in the rock. I shall not remain here, but go south again.

The god sits above me in his temple and stands above me in the sky and shines upwards from the surface of the sea. To do this requires a simultaneity which is no problem to gods. It is a matter of time which is a circle and space which, like life, curls to bite its own tail. Death, it seems, follows the same pattern.

The god appears to be an orb; his bow is curved, his lyre a double curve, a space between wings, and I, for one, shall leave him in his place. Let him curve down into the night and up into tomorrow. I have never been in doubt that it is simply ordered, a nautilus shell containing that which is. I accept that it is all quite simple. I am sure it is quite simple. The partridge I can see, through half-closed eyes, strutting in the grass. Is it the soul of Talos, or a sign my sister sends, or the attribute of a goddess, or a little curved and rounded bird taking no interest in such things? I must go southwards, curving back to the place where Minos will meet me; and in Sicily I shall contrive something to thwart him.

Grief is coming in upon me slowly. It finds its way through the cracks and fissures of the mould in which I am cast and I feel it coat the clay. I am perplexed and I shall say nothing more here. I am sure that all things are ordered and I shall presently grasp the design of these things which concern us here. I shall leave all this that I have written down, burying it under the rock.

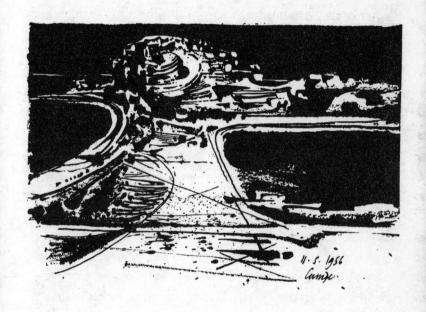

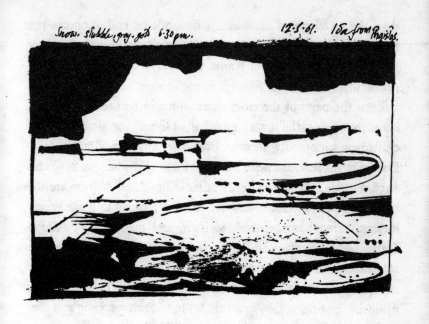

Snow. stubble. gray. gold 6.30 pm.   12·5·61.   Ida from Praxiles.

Postscript

This narrative occurred. I did not set out to write it nor to impose upon the simple antique legend the web of supposition which has come to clothe it for me during the four years of my obsessive concern with Daedalus and his son. Many things came together, in an equation of the mysteries of remote antiquity with the implications of the age in which we live. The legend, for three thousand years or more a fiction handed down, has in our own time become descriptive of the actual experience. Men fly and men go further than the envelope of air which surrounds us and supports the flight of birds. In all the time since the ancients wove the myth of flight round Daedalus and Icarus, it has been depicted either as a dream or as the merest folly. It is not so now.

Even the parts of the story came to me in no order. I did not know that Talos, the brazen guardian of Crete, was also Talos the craftsman supposedly thrown from the Athenian Acropolis by Daedalus, his jealous uncle. I did not know this when, in 1955 and 1956, I made two bronze heads called *Talos I* and *II* from animal bones and plaster, cast in bronze. In 1958 I began to make reliefs in wax, using bones embedded in it, and made my first large Icarus relief sculpture in which the wings are formed from the vertebrae of fish. At this time I did not know anything about the saw invented either by Talos or Daedalus which, in legend, was made by casting a fish-spine in bronze. Perhaps Jung's is the explanation for this sort of memory, if that is what it is.

The legend grew in me, forced itself upon me and emerged in the form of reliefs, bronzes, drawings and paintings in various media. At times in Greece and Crete in 1958 an unexpected compulsion to write scraps of verse came over me. These, too, came in no sort of order, and not especially in the context of the legend. The landscape, lizards on the rocks and perhaps especially the hawks wheeling in the sky prompted these compositions at a time when the Greek landscape first possessed me. Delos especially exercised upon me an intense compulsion. I travelled in various ways. By boat I visited many of the islands and I have flown from Crete to the mainland and from Greece to Italy a number of times. In the course of all this and with the unseen presence of the fledgling astronaut, at that time poised to go into space, in some obscure way always with me, I became entangled in this particular myth. Perhaps it is because the flight of Daedalus and Icarus has a relevance to the twentieth century more piercing even than most myths which, being universal, are always relevant at any time to man's existence. I say I became entangled in this myth because I did not choose it consciously as a good subject. That is not how I work. Landscape, the sea, birds, young men diving from high rocks, photos in the press of astronauts in training being submitted to tests for pressure at simulated high velocities, athletes, the little geometric bronzes of the period archaeologists call 'Daedalic', the Minoan archaeological sites and their association with Daedalus as legendary architect, inventor and craftsman reflecting back upon our own age of technological miracles, all played some part in creating in me a frame of relevant thought. I have always had recurring dreams of flight. When I was a schoolboy I had a passion for early aeronautics. My father was a classicist who used to tell me about the Greeks and the Homeric legends in my early childhood. I don't know how much or how little these things have to do with it.

I do know that we live by myth, inventing it when necessary, returning to it with satisfaction when it seems useful. Who is Icarus? The pilots I envied in general and found intolerable in particular when I was in the R.A.F. in the most humble and slightly ludicrous capacity, immediately after the Battle of Britain? I watched them when no one in command could find any use for such abilities as I might possess and I lived in a mist of boredom. Is Icarus the perpetual hero who, given more, dares more than normal men and therefore seems a little childish? And who is Daedalus, the *polytechnos*, 'maker of things', greatest mythical progenitor, after Prometheus, of what the artist is? He is also the cunning man, creator and trickster, thinking faster and better than others, yet a man whose sensitivity runs counter to his intelligence and who is intelligently aware of his failure in sensitivity. Is not he, too, perpetual?

All these things revolved in my brain around the axis of a simple tale in which a man made wings to get himself out of a difficult situation and took his son with him from Crete towards Cumae by air, in prehistoric times. The son ignored his father's warning, flew too near the sun and the wings his father had made for him melted and came apart. Icarus fell into the sea and was drowned. That is all there is in mythology about Icarus. To me that is where it started, but curiously it started at the wrong end, for the germination took place on the beach below the Acropolis of Cumae, north of Naples, where Virgil tells us Daedalus landed at the end of his flight. I had not at that time been to Greece. It was in 1956 and I was the most devoted Italophile and wanted nowhere else. I made drawings and several paintings of Cumae and then went north to Rome.

I was in Greece and Crete for much of 1958. Drawings and reliefs came first and it was not until 1959 that I painted the first of the *Icarus Falls* series and made the first two of fifteen bronzes concerned with the Icarus theme. Fourteen of these bronzes and thirty-five paintings and drawings, including many landscapes of Crete and the Cyclades, were exhibited at the Matthiesen Gallery in London in October 1961. Sometime early in 1960 I assembled the scraps of verse I had written and began to write the Daedalus narrative around them, rewriting them, again and again, into what I came to call the 'Songs of Icarus'.

In the course of writing this narrative, while rewriting and extending the verse, the extended sequence of events – or my conception of events, which is permissible when mythmaking – came into being and I realized that I must explain for myself the relationship between Daedalus and his son and the passion Icarus had for Apollo. Those images in which I came to portray Icarus at the climax of his flight, in suicidal contact with the sun itself, are the result of the narrative. The narrative, on the other hand, is the result of many previous images, the reliefs, bronzes, drawings and paintings out of which it grew.

The drawings reproduced here are not book illustrations in the normal sense. They were drawn at various times between 1955 and 1962 and were part of the process of discovering what happened. Some are studies for bronze sculptures, which changed in the course of execution, but these are not too remote from their final versions. *Daedalus Winged*, the *Talos Head*, *Icarus Drowned* and *Daedalus at Cumae* are all recognizably related to the bronzes which are now scattered about in English, French and American collections. Some of the drawings are studies for paintings, some for relief sculptures, some exist simply as drawings, such as the double-eyed image of *Minos Masked* and the *Scream*, which were produced during the writing of the narrative in order that I should *see* what I was talking about.

The vital problem for me has been the figure of Icarus at the time-stopped climax of his flight and what happened to him when he coupled with the sun. I had to evolve his shape as he rose and then combine in a single image the aspiration and the disaster, the triumph and defeat and the paradox of motionlessness at high velocity. I had to make his rise implicit in his fall and to make him both adequate and inadequate, heroic and ridiculous. Groping for this crucial image, I made a great quantity of drawings and those illustrated here, plates 6 to 15, are simply a selection from the work in progress. I have never found the totality, or succeeded finally in matching what I *know* Daedalus saw happen to what I myself can realize in paint or bronze. Thus I am as defeated as Icarus and the curious mass of images I have made are shards of the whole. Yet how could they be otherwise when even Daedalus himself was defeated? Twice, Virgil maintains, he tried to depict his son's fate upon the golden doors of the new Temple to Apollo he raised upon the rock at Cumae and twice his craft failed him in his grief.

He left his wings in the Temple, dedicating them to the god and then, according to Diodorus Siculus, he journeyed on to Sicily. In Sicily he lived as the guest of Cocalus and his name is associated also with the rise of the cities of Gela and Akragas. He made sculptures and erected buildings and the city of Palma is possibly that which was once called Daedalium in his honour.

The final and inevitable meeting between Minos and Daedalus

came when Minos and the Cretan fleet arrived at Camicus, for there it was that Minos employed a stratagem to cause Daedalus to reveal himself. He offered Cocalus a triton shell, promising to reward the man who could thread it with linen, because he knew that only Daedalus could accomplish this feat. Daedalus, perhaps with the bitter memory of the nautilus still in him, took the shell and bored a hole in its smallest spiral. He then smeared its larger convolution with honey. Taking a strand of gossamer he attached it to an ant and the linen thread he fastened to the gossamer. He introduced the ant through the hole he had bored and the ant, dragging gossamer and thread, pursued the honey through all the intricacies of the shell so that all the spirals of the triton were thus threaded. Daedalus gave the threaded shell to Cocalus who claimed the reward, whereupon Minos demanded that Daedalus be delivered into his hands. However Cocalus would not give him up and together Cocalus and Daedalus murdered Minos by piping boiling water into his bath so that Minos was scalded to death. The Sicilians then burned the Cretan fleet. The journey of Daedalus thereafter took him to Sardinia and there the legend ends, or if it does not then Daedalus is still with us. I have added these events to this postscript because they belong here since his testament ended at Cumae and in any case I only sought out this information when I had finished the narrative.

On the day I completed the Testament, a man was put into orbit and on the day I received the galley proofs and added this paragraph, the first man-powered flight, sustained over half a mile, was announced, so that it seems that the brain of Daedalus and the sinews of Icarus maintain their paradoxical duality. Tomorrow I return to Crete.

I wish I was sure that I am free of Icarus and that I have enough of that part of Daedalus in me to make good images. The artist, 'the maker of things', seeks to represent some part of what he thinks man is, and was, in order to discover himself in the process: or so I believe. Perhaps he also hopes to extend man's experience of himself – by strapping some kind of wings on him – but this would be a fortunate chance and is not the crux of the matter.

MICHAEL AYRTON
May 1962

Plates

1. *Daedalus winged*, pen and wash drawing, 14″×20″ 1959
2. *Icarus*, wash drawing, 11½″×11″ 1961
3. *Icarus winged*, pen drawing, 17½″×11½″ 1960
4. *Icarus rising*, monochrome oil sketch, 23½″×19½″ 1960
5. *Night sea*, monotype, 19″×14″ 1962
6. *Talos*, monotype, 12″×10″ 1955
7. *Icarus held*, pen drawing, 19½″×12½″ 1960
8. *Head at high velocity*, pen drawing, 8″×10″ 1959
9. *Scream*, pen drawing, 10″×8″ 1961
10. *Icarus transformed*, pen drawing, 9½″×11½″ 1961
11. *Icarus at the climax*, pen drawing, 10″×8″ 1961
12. *Icarus suspended*, brush drawing, 15″×17½″ 1958
13. *Icarus disintegrated*, monotype, 21½″×14½″ 1962
14. *Icarus falls*, pen drawing, 22″×14″ 1960
15. *Icarus drowned*, monotype, 20″×14″ 1962
16. *Daedalus at Cumae*, pen drawing, 15″×11″ 1961

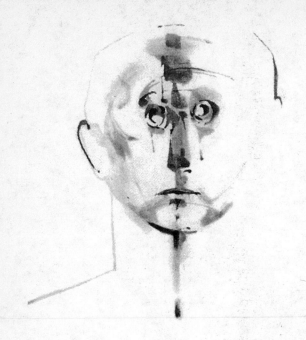

23·10·64

michel gautier
23 3 1960.

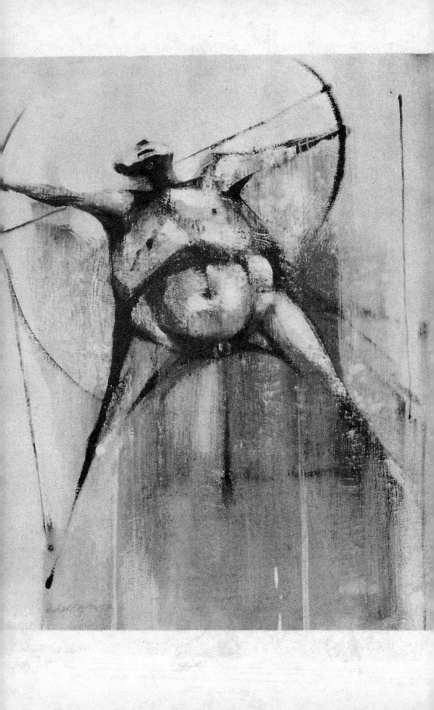

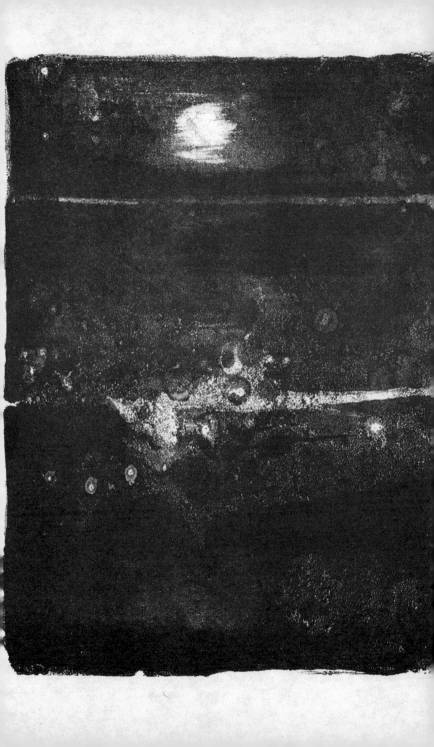

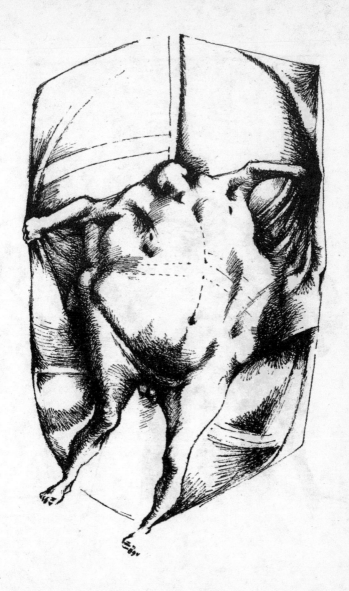

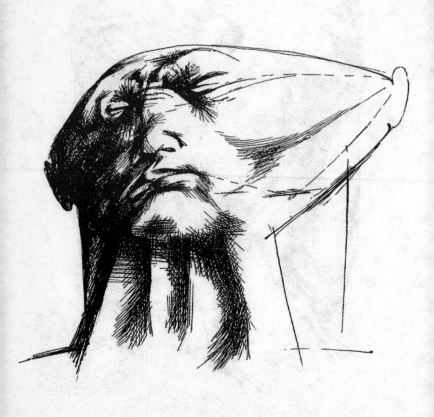

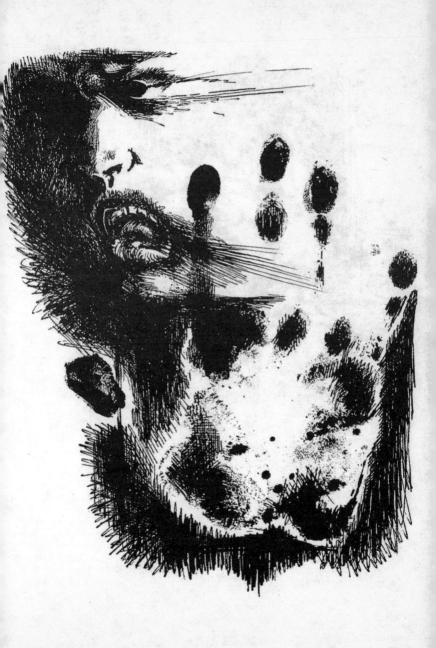

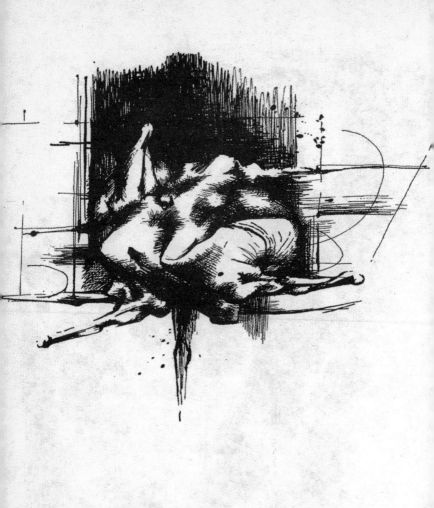

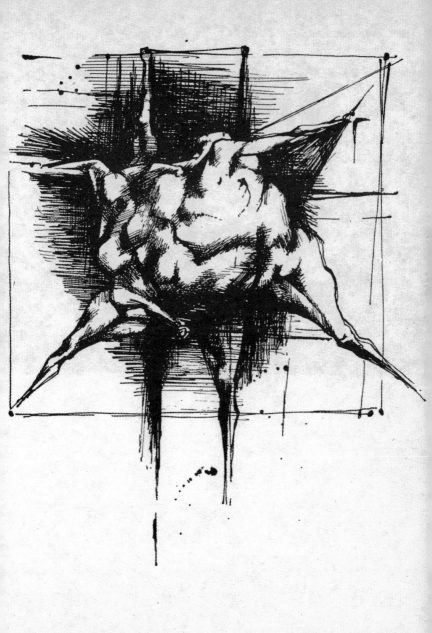

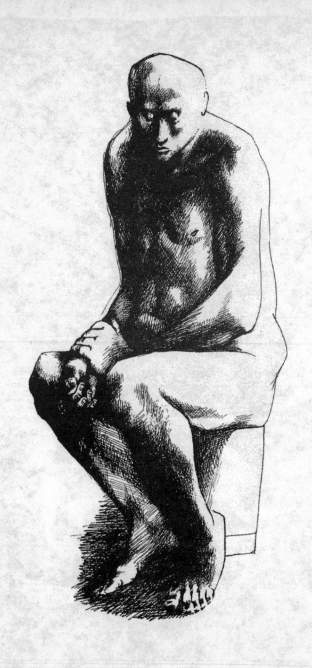